The Very Helpful Little Octopus

A Little Animal Adventure

The Very Helpful Little Octopus

Written by Christina Wilsdon
Illustrations by Tom Brannon

Published by The Reader's Digest Association Limited
London ❖ New York ❖ Sydney ❖ Montreal

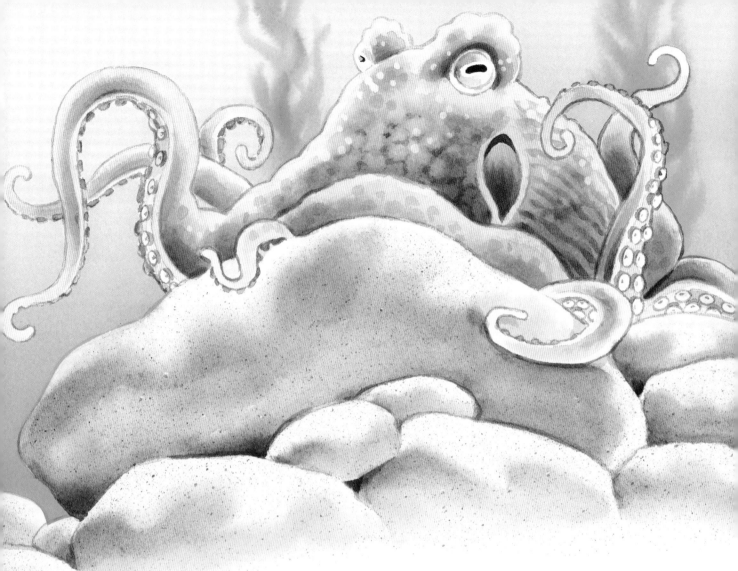

Little Octopus was going to visit his aunt. He paused at the bottom of a big rock as he was leaving home.

'Goodbye, Mum,' he called.

'Goodbye, Little Octopus,' answered his mother, peering over the top of the rock. 'Say "hello" to Auntie Octopus for me.'

'I will,' said Little Octopus as he raced away through streamers of seaweed.

It was a sunny day and the water was warm. Little Octopus hummed as he swam.

'Good morning,' he called to a bed of oysters.

'It's not a very good morning for me,' replied one of the oysters sadly.

'Why not?' asked Little Octopus.

'I've lost my pearl,' cried the oyster. 'It rolled out when I opened my shell this morning and fell between the rocks.'

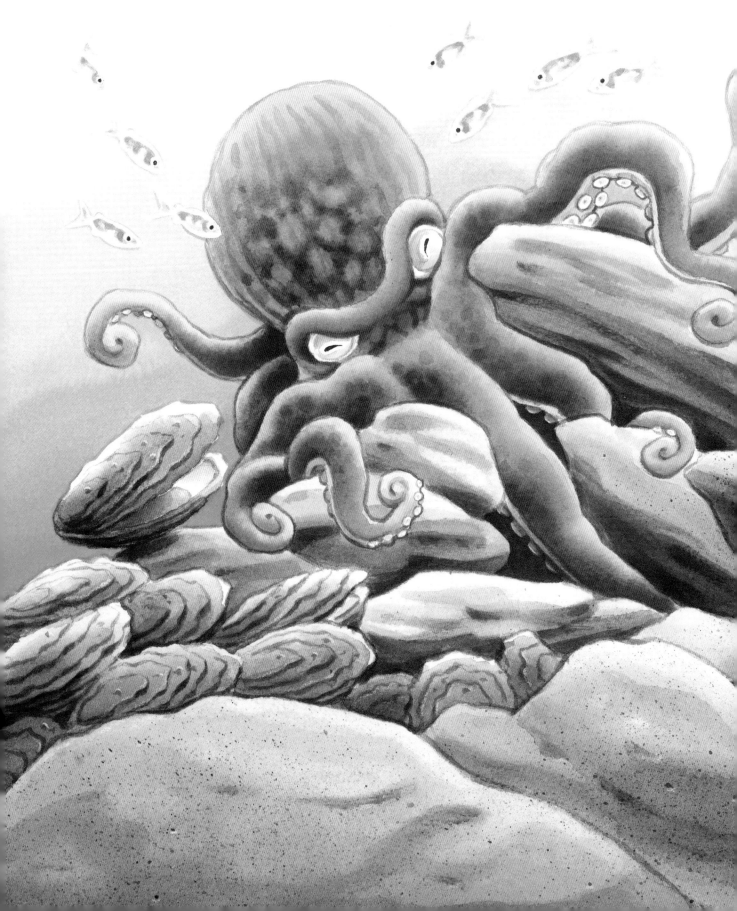

Little Octopus peered into the narrow, dark space. He could see the shiny glint of a pearl at the bottom.

'I think I can reach it,' said Little Octopus.

He stretched an arm as far as he could and felt around.

'Got it,' he shouted.

'Hooray!' cheered the oysters as Little Octopus returned the pearl to its owner.

'Thank you very much,' said the oyster. 'That's brilliant!'

Little Octopus hurried on his way. He spotted a seal pup zooming through the water.

'Hello, Little Seal,' he said.

'Hello, Little Octopus,' said the seal sadly. She seemed upset.

'What's wrong?' asked Little Octopus.

'I've lost my family,' said the seal. 'I've been poking my head out of the water to find them – but I can't see them anywhere.'

'Maybe I can help,' said Little Octopus. 'I'll push you up so you can see farther.'

They swam to the surface and he lifted the seal with two of his arms and held her high above the waves.

'What a great idea, Little Octopus. I can see them,' cried Little Seal. 'They're way over there, sunning themselves on the rocks. Thanks.'

She splashed back into the water and swam towards them.

'I'm going to be late if I keep stopping to help other animals,' said Little Octopus to himself.

'Hi, there,' he called as he swam near a group of baby fish. Noticing their sad faces, he asked, 'What's the matter?'

'We're stuck,' said one fish, showing him a wide and busy crack in the ocean floor where other fish were quickly swimming in both directions. 'We're not allowed to cross to the other side unless a big fish goes with us.'

'Well, I'm not a fish, but I'm big enough,' said Little Octopus proudly. 'And I can hold on to all of you. Come on.'

'Thank you,' said the tiny fish.

'Look right, look left, then right again,' said Little Octopus. They waited for a break in the traffic, then crossed the opening safely.

Little Octopus waved goodbye to the fish as he sped away.

'That has to be my last stop,' he told himself firmly.

But it wasn't. There was a quick stop to help an eel who had tied himself into a knot ... and another stop to help a hermit crab to find a bigger shell to live in ... and one more to help a starfish up onto the top of a high rock.

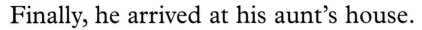

Finally, he arrived at his aunt's house.

'Hi, Auntie Octopus. Sorry I'm late,' called Little Octopus, as he tumbled into her rocky home.

'What happened? Are you okay?' asked Auntie Octopus, giving him a big hug.

'Oh, I'm fine,' said Little Octopus. 'I just had to stop to lend a hand to a few creatures who needed help.'

'Good for you,' said Auntie Octopus. 'I'm proud of you for helping. That's a very good reason for being a little late.'

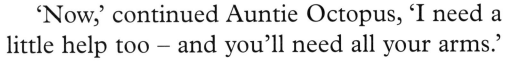

'Now,' continued Auntie Octopus, 'I need a little help too – and you'll need all your arms.'

'That's why I came,' said Little Octopus.

He opened his arms wide. Auntie Octopus gently placed a dear little, wriggling baby octopus in each one.

'Eight new cousins!' exclaimed Little Octopus. He cuddled them close, humming quietly as he rocked them to sleep.

All about ... **OCTOPUSES**

FACT FILE
NEW FOR OLD
An octopus can grow a new arm, or tentacle, to replace one that is lost.

CLEVER CAMOUFLAGE
Octopuses can change colour. Sometimes they change to match their surroundings. An angry octopus may turn red!

SECRET WEAPON
An octopus squirts a cloud of ink into the water when it is under attack from predators. The ink cloud surprises its enemy and gives the octopus time to escape.

TINY BABY
A baby octopus is only about 0.5 centimetres long when it hatches – about the size of an ant.

SCARY MONSTER
The giant Pacific octopus is the world's biggest octopus. It can grow to be 10 metres wide.

BUSY MOTHER
A female octopus lays about 20,000 eggs. She hangs these in strings, guarding them and keeping them clean for about a month before they hatch.

The Very Helpful Little Octopus is a Little Animal Adventures book
published by Reader's Digest Young Families, Inc.
by arrangement with Éditions Nathan, Paris, France

Written by Christina Wilsdon
Illustrations by Tom Brannon
Notebook artwork © Paul Bommer

This edition was adapted and published in 2008 by
The Reader's Digest Association Limited
11 Westferry Circus, Canary Wharf, London E14 4HE

We are committed to both the quality of our products
and the service we provide to our customers.
We value your comments, so please feel free to contact us on
08705 113366 or via our website at:
www.readersdigest.co.uk
If you have any comments or suggestions about the content of our books,
you can contact us at:
gbeditorial@readersdigest.co.uk

Printed in China

Book code: 637-016 UP0000-1
ISBN: 978 0 276 44348 0
Oracle code: 501800105H.00.24